Challenge your pupils 2
using problem-solving questions from the
Primary Mathematics Challenge

The Mathematical Association

First published in 2012 by
The Mathematical Association

ISBN 978-0-906588-72-7

Printed in Great Britain by Executive Image (Leicester) Ltd

How to use this book

These problems can be used in several different ways. Here are a few ideas:

1.   selected by the teacher for homework, either choosing particular topics or at random
2.   extension work in class, selecting problems relating to classwork
3.   selecting a problem as a starter for investigative work
4.   practice for the papers set in PMC which take place every November (primary schools only).

The problems

Over 200 multiple choice problems from a variety of mathematical topics are provided for use by teachers in primary (and secondary) schools. The aim is to provide interesting mathematical experiences using elementary mathematics topics. Many of the problems can lead to further investigative work.

There are four categories of problems: Easy, Harder, Puzzling and Very Challenging. Most pupils should be able to get the easy problems correct, while the challenging problems will test the brightest young mathematicians in the country!

A few of the harder problems are not multiple choice as in the PMC papers – pupils must just find the answer without guessing!

Answers and Notes

Answers and brief notes are provided for all problems. There are also some ideas for follow up work and extended investigation.

Mathematical Health Warning!

The difficult and challenging problems in this book are difficult! Problems for each pupil should first be selected from the Easy section, and then to progress to the more difficult problems, rather than start with the harder problems. If pupils cannot get a grip on the harder multiple choice problems, they will just guess!

Contents

Easy Problems

E1   Which of these calculations does not give the answer 73 ?

   A 7 + 3   B 70 + 3   C 100 − 27   D 80 − 7   E 73 × 1

E2   Which has the biggest answer?

   A 7 × 4   B 6 × 5   C 2 × 5   D 15 + 16   E $\frac{1}{2}$ of 60

E3   1 + 2 + 3 + 3 + 2 + 1 =

   A 11   B 12   C 13   D 14   E 15

E4   I am thinking of a number. When I add two
   to it, I get 12. What is my number?

   A 2   B 10   C 12   D 14   E 20

E5   A quarter of a number is 12. What is the number?

   A 3   B 6   C 12   D 24   E 48

E6   When I divide 123 by 5, what remainder do I get?
   A 0   B 1   C 2   D 3   E 4

E7   Calculate 8 × 6 × 4 × 2 × 0.
   A 0   B 20   C 196   D 384   E 86420

E8   Which answer is the largest number?

   A 1 + 2 + 3   B 1 × 2 + 3   C 1 + 2 − 3   D $\frac{1}{2}$ × 3   E 2 × 3 + 1

E9   In a typical class of 30 children, what would there be most of?

   A fingers   B hairs   C knees   D thumbs   E toes

E10 My rule is double the number, add 4 and then divide by 2.
   If I start with the number 12, what is my answer?
   A 6   B 8   C 12   D 14   E 28

E11 Which of these numbers divides exactly into 2007?

   A 3   B 4   C 5   D 6   E 7

Easy Problems

E12 I think of a number, multiply it by three, subtract zero from it and get zero as my answer. What was my number?

A 0 B 1 C 3 D 6 E 10

E13 If 2 CLICK 3 means double 2 and add 3, what is the value of 4 CLICK 5?

A 1 B 9 C 13 D 14 E 18

E14 My rule is 'multiply by three and then subtract 4'. My answer is 5. What number did I start with?

A 1 B 2 C 3 D 4 E 5

E15 Which of these questions doesn't give the answer 4?

A $\frac{1}{2}$ of 8 B $\frac{1}{4}$ of 12 C 12 − 8 D 16 ÷ 4 E double 2

E16 The 99 Pence Shop Company has all goods priced at 99p. How much do 7 cost?

A £0.93 B £0.99 C £6.93 D £7.93 E £7.99

E17 Bob's car has a 60 litre petrol tank which is empty. Petrol goes up from £1.27 to £1.37 a litre. How much more does it cost Bob to fill up his car?

A 60p B £6 C £60 D £600 E £6000

E18 Which of these units could be used to measure how much food my cat eats?
A miles per hour   B £ per person
C razor blades per year   D words per m²
E tins per week

E19 How many £2 coins would you need to make £20?

A 2 B 4 C 6 D 8 E 10

Easy Problems

E20 If Gurtek is 8 years old and Surjeet is half her age, what age will Surjeet be when Gurtek is 20?

    A 10   B 16   C 24   D 30   E 40

E21 This clock is accurate but upside down. What time is it?

    A 1.15   B 3.05   C 6.45   D 12.15   E 12.45

E22 Knitty Knora takes 55 minutes to knit a scarf. How long will it take her to knit six scarves?

    A 3 hr 30 min   B 5 hr 30 min
    C 5 hr 50 min   D 6 hr 30 min
    E none of these

E23 Anna Nokemova scores 10 points for the first skittle she knocks over, 9 points for the second one, 8 points for the third one, and so on.
Altogether, she knocks over six skittles. How many points does she get?

    A 6   B 15   C 36   D 45   E 60

E24 My teenage brother plays on his computer game for 15 hours each day. How many hours will he have played on his computer in a week?

    A 7   B 15   C 49   D 105   E 360

E25 Titus the Tortoise is training for the 2012 Olympics. Which of these speeds is the fastest?

    A 5 miles in 3 hours   B 3 miles in 5 hours
    C 3 miles in 3 hours   D 5 miles in 5 hours
    E the speeds are all the same

Easy Problems

E26 If the day before yesterday was Sunday, what will the day after tomorrow be?

A Wednesday   B Thursday   C Friday
D Saturday   E Sunday

E27 Slinky the lazy snail crawls seven millimetres every hour. If she keeps up this rate for seven hours, how far will she have travelled altogether?

A 7mm   B 7cm   C 4.9cm   D 49cm   E 77km

E28 Approximately how tall is the average woman?

A 1.70m   B 2.70m   C 3.70m   D 4.70m   E 5.70m

E29 If Stefan's height is approximately seven times the length of his foot and his foot is 21cm long, how tall is he likely to be?

A 3cm   B 14.7cm   C 147cm   D 180cm   E 3m

E30 Rosie plants a row of five roses, equally spaced, stretching 60cm in a straight line. How long is the space between two roses?

A 5cm   B 10cm   C 12cm   D 15cm   E 60cm

E31 Approximately what is the height of an average ant?

A 1mm   B 1 foot   C 1m   D 1km   E 1 mile

E32 Nine elephants stood in some fresh concrete. How many foot prints were made?

A 9   B 18   C 27   D 36   E 45

E33 As you know, you need a partner to be in the three-legged race. What is the smallest number of people that would be needed for a three-legged race?

A 1   B 2   C 3   D 4   E 6

Easy Problems

E34 In the window of his shop Mr Cannit always stacks his tins in triangular patterns. Which of these could not be the number of tins in one of his stacks?

A 15   B 22   C 28   D 36   E 45

E35 Which of these words best describes the probability of a £1 coin standing on its edge after it has been spun through the air?

A impossible   B very unlikely   C evens
D likely   E certain

E36 I cut a hexagon like this into two pieces. I cut from one vertex (corner) to another. One piece is a triangle. What shape must the other piece be?

A triangle   B square   C pentagon
D hexagon   E rectangle

E37 Forget the eye. One pupil called this shape a headagon. What is its correct name?

A circle   B kite   C nonagon   D square   E rectangle

E38 Here is a drawing of a man. Which of these shapes is not in the drawing?
A triangle   B square   C rectangle
D circle   E pentagon

E39 Which of these objects has the shortest perimeter?

A   B   C   D   E

E40 An octopus has eight tentacles. How many tentacles do eighty-eight octopi have?

A 64   B 88   C 704   D 888   E 6464

Easy Problems

E41 Which of these shapes has three sides?

A kite   B rectangle C rhombus D square   E triangle

E42 What fraction of this zebra crossing is shaded black?

A $\dfrac{3}{4}$ B $\dfrac{4}{3}$ C $\dfrac{3}{7}$ D $\dfrac{4}{7}$ E $\dfrac{7}{7}$

E43 How many ▭ are there in ⬜ ?

A 4   B 6   C 8   D 12   E 24

E44 A regular hexagon has a perimeter of 60cm. How long is each side?

A 10cm   B 12cm   C 15cm   D 20cm   E 30cm

E45 Here is a drawing of our cat. Which drawing shows the cat rotated 90 degrees anticlockwise?

A   B   C   D   E

E46 Each shape in this net is a rhombus. Which one of these 3-d shapes can be made from the net?

A   B   C

D   E

E47 Polly Gonn has two pieces of wood with the same shape. She fits them together without overlapping. Which shape can she NOT make?

A   B   C   D   E

E48 Which word has correct spelling?

A kube   B squarre   C triangel
D subtrakshun   E multiplication

Harder Problems

H1   The value of $100 - 99 + 98 - 97 + \ldots + 2 - 1$ is

A 0   B 50   C 100   D 1010   E 5050

H2   Calculate $3 + 2 + 1 + 0 + (-1) + (-2) + (-3)$

A −12   B −6   C 0   D 6   E 12

H3   Trixie says "My number is still a three digit number if I divide it by three or multiply it by three." Which number could it be?

A 282   B 318   C 336   D 363   E 369

H4   I have £6 to share equally between seven people. How much is left over?

A 5p   B 7p   C 10p   D £1   E nothing

H5   What is the value of $10 - 9 + 8 - 7 + 6 - 5 + 4 - 3 + 2 - 1$?

A −5   B 0   C 5   D 50   E 54

H6   One of these numbers is a prime number. Which one?

A 113   B 114   C 115   D 116   E 117

H7   Which of these numbers is not a factor of 2010?

A 6   B 10   C 12   D 15   E 67

H8   I multiply two prime numbers together. What answer can I **not** get?

A 8   B 14   C 15   D 21   E 22

H9   How many of these additions are equal to 1 ?

$$\frac{1}{2} + \frac{1}{2} \qquad \frac{1}{3} + \frac{1}{3} + \frac{1}{3} \qquad \frac{1}{4} + \frac{1}{4} + \frac{1}{4} + \frac{1}{4} \qquad \frac{1}{5} + \frac{1}{5} + \frac{1}{5} + \frac{1}{5} + \frac{1}{5}$$

A 0   B 1   C 2   D 3   E 4

H10   Which of these fractions is nearest to 1?

A $\dfrac{5}{6}$ B $\dfrac{6}{7}$ C $\dfrac{7}{8}$ D $\dfrac{23}{24}$ E $\dfrac{99}{100}$

Harder Problems

H11 What is the value of $\dfrac{\frac{3}{5} + \frac{1}{5}}{\frac{2}{5}}$?

     A 2   B 3   C 4   D 5   E 6

H12 What is the value of $\dfrac{54}{4\frac{1}{5} + 1\frac{4}{5}}$?

     A 4   B 6   C 9   D 45   E 54

H13 The value of $\dfrac{1}{2}$ of $\dfrac{2}{3}$ is:

     A $\dfrac{1}{6}$ B $\dfrac{1}{4}$ C $\dfrac{1}{3}$ D $\dfrac{3}{8}$ E $\dfrac{1}{2}$

H14 Which of the following statements is true?

     A 333 333 is divisible by 2   B 444 444 is divisible by 3
     C 555 555 is divisible by 4   D 666 666 is divisible by 5
     E 777 777 is divisible by 6

H15 The sum of two numbers is 9 and the product of the same two numbers is 18. What is the difference between them?

     A 2   B 3   C 4   D 5   E 6

H16 In this multiplication, what is the asterisked digit which makes it correct?

$$\begin{array}{r} 3 \; * \; 4 \\ 5 \; \times \\ \hline 1\,6\,7\,0 \end{array}$$

     A 1   B 3   C 4   D 5   E 7

H17 There are two numbers, a and b. If $a + b = 10$ and $a - b = 2$, what is a ?

     A 2   B 4   C 6   D 8   E 10

H18 Bing and Bang are different numbers. Bing × Bang = Bang, Bing × Bing = Bing, and Bing + Bing = Bang. What is Bang × Bang?

     A 0   B 1   C 2   D 3   E 4

Harder Problems

H19 What is the missing number?

        24 20 16 ….. 8

  A 4   B 8   C 12   D 16   E 20

H20 1 is the first odd number, 3 is the second and so on…
If I add together the eighth, ninth and tenth odd numbers what do I get?

  A 21   B 31   C 41   D 51   E 61

H21 In which of these did New Year's Day and Christmas Day fall in the same year?

  A 2005   B 2006   C 2007
  D None of these   E All of these

H22 I am designing a rectangular milk crate which I don't want to be long and thin. Which of these would be the best number of bottles to fill the crate?

  A 11   B 13   C 15   D 17   E 19

H23 I am thinking of three numbers. When I add them together I get the same result as if I multiply them together. What could my three numbers be?

  A 0, 1, 2   B 1, 1, 1   C 1, 2, 3   D 1, 2, 4   E 1, 4, 2

H24 I roll five dice once and add the scores. What is the difference between the highest total and the lowest total I could get?

  A 5   B 20   C 25   D 29   E 30

H25 Bill lives with 3 cats, 4 birds and one snake. How many legs are there altogether?

  A 2   B 12   C 22   D 38   E 42

Harder Problems

H26 I have three hens. Ginger lays one egg a day, Rocky lays one every two days and Bunty lays one every three days. How many eggs altogether will the three hens lay in 12 days?

    A 3   B 12   C 22   D 24   E 36

H27 If three people give each other birthday cards during the year, they need six cards altogether.

How many cards will be needed in one year if five people give each other cards?

    A 4   B 5   C 10   D 20   E 40

H28 Some girls bought necklaces with their names on. Alice paid £2.50 for her necklace, Rie paid £1.50 for hers and Isobel paid £3 for hers. How much did Mackenzie have to pay for her necklace?

    A £1.50   B £2.50   C £3.50   D £4.50   E £5.50

H29 One Friday, Miss Fivefroots gives all the children in her class 2 cherries. There are 28 children in her class and 12 cherries in a packet.

How many packets of cherries does Miss Fivefroots need to buy to give each child two cherries?

    A 2   B 3   C 4   D 5   E 6

H30 Alice said, "I am thinking of a 2-digit whole number. It is a multiple of four and a multiple of five but not a multiple of six".

How many 2-digit whole numbers fit this description?

    A 1   B 2   C 3   D 4   E 20

H31 Mick Sterbs planted a number of courgette seeds. 60% of them germinated and grew into 12 plants. How many seeds did Mick plant?

    A 6   B 12   C 20   D 24   E 30

Harder Problems

H32 Jenny wants to go to the shops and has one each of these coins:
1p, 2p, 5p, 10p and 20p.
What coin do I need to give her so she can make all the amounts up to and including 40p?

A 1p   B 2p   C 5p   D 10p   E 20p

H33 Mrs Bun the baker sells buns at the school gate for 10p each, or 4 for the price of 3, or 12 for price of 8. What is the cheapest price for 30 buns?

A £2.00   B £2.10   C £2.20   D £2.30   E £3.00

H34 Penny Pound has a collection of 2p coins which she is able to balance in a tower, one on top of each other. The tower stretches up 1 metre high. Approximately how many coins are there in the tower?

A 10   B 50   C 100   D 500   E 2000

H35 Many years ago, before electric and gas lights, teachers used candles! One teacher used a candle clock which went down 2cm in an hour. How many cm did it go down from 6.15pm to 9.30pm?

A 3   B 4   C 6   D 6.5   E 7.5

H36 Apparently, the average person in the UK uses 1200 metres of toilet paper in a year. How many kilometres of paper would Mr Average use by his 80th birthday?

A 80   B 96   C 1000   D 1200   E 96 000

H37 At the Priory Friery, a monk is selling monkfish at £20 a kilo.
Another monk buys a piece that weighs 200g.
How much does he pay?

A £2   B £4   C £5   D £10   E £20

11

Harder Problems

H38 During March 2006 Harriet Hothead said, "I am ten years old but I've only had two 'proper' birthdays!" On what date was Harriet born?

A 28 February 1996   B 29 February 1996
C 1 March 1996   D 2 March 1996
E 3 March 1996

H39 Doctor When travels through time. She enters her time machine SIDRAT in 2007, travels to 2107, then to 1907 and finally to 2057.
Through how many years has she travelled in total?

A 50   B 150   C 250   D 450   E 8078

H40 W, X, Y and Z are in the middle of the sides of the square.
What fraction of the square is shaded?

A $\dfrac{1}{8}$ B $\dfrac{1}{4}$ C $\dfrac{3}{8}$ D $\dfrac{3}{4}$ E $\dfrac{1}{2}$

H41 Which of these solids has one curved surface and two flat surfaces?

A cone   B cuboid   C cylinder   D pyramid   E sphere

H42 The flag for Guyana is a rectangle with red, green and yellow sections.
What fraction of the flag is shaded green?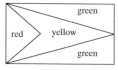

A $\frac{1}{8}$ B $\frac{1}{4}$ C $\frac{1}{3}$ D $\frac{1}{2}$ E $\frac{2}{3}$

H43 You go into this maze by the arrow. If you move one square according to the direction shown each time, where will you come out of the maze?

A 1   B 2   C 3   D 4   E 5

Harder Problems

H44 This mouse knows how many of these mini-cheeses fit into this container. How many do you think will fit?

2cm 45° 5cm _ 10cm . 4cm

| A 6 | B 8 | C 10 | D 12 | E 16 |

H45 A rectangular pond is cut into the middle of a small rectangular lawn. The lawn is 8m × 5m and the pond is 5m × 3m.
What is the area of the grass that is left?

| A $6m^2$ | B $10m^2$ | C $20m^2$ | D $25m^2$ | E $55m^2$ |

H46 How many of these shapes have rotational symmetry of order 4 ?

| A 0 | B 1 | C 2 | D 3 | E 4 |

H47 I have six equilateral triangles, each with a perimeter of 12cm. I fit them together to make a regular hexagon. What is the hexagon's perimeter?

| A 6cm | B 12cm | C 24cm | D 36cm | E 72cm |

H48 The two side views and the top view for a 3d shape are:

What is the name of the shape?

A cylinder B cube   C cuboid   D pyramid   E sphere

H49 The diagram is made up of a rectangle and an equilateral triangle. What is the size of the angle marked × ?

| A 30° | B 45° | C 50° | D 60° | E 70° |

H50 All the squares in these shapes are of the same size. Which shape has the shortest perimeter?

A   B   C   D   E

13

Harder Problems

H51 This spiral is drawn on a regular one centimetre lattice and starts at *A*. How long will the spiral be (in cm) to reach the point marked *X* ?

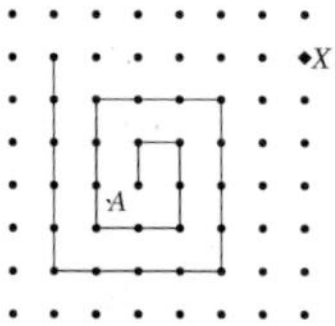

A 28 B 56 C 57 D 64 E 72

H52 I was facing north when my mother made me eat a very sour apple which turned my head through 405° anticlockwise.

In which direction was my head facing after eating the apple?

A E B NE C N D NW E W

H53 Flutterly Butterly is aiming south as it flies at 5 mph. The wind is blowing from east to west at 5 mph. In which direction will the butterfly be actually going?

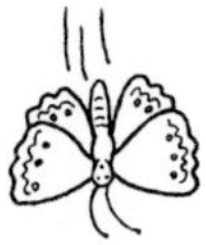

A NE B NW C S D SE E SW

H54 Rob Burr was driving his car. He sees a police car in his mirror. Which of these would he see in his mirror?

A ƎƆI⅃Oꟼ B EƆILOꟼ C EƆI⅃Oꟼ D ƎƆI⅃OP E ECILOP

H55 Can't, Don't, Shan't and Won't are in trouble for arguing about doing their homework. Can't argued for longer than Shan't; Won't argued longer than Don't; Shan't argued for longer than Won't. Who argued the least time?

A Can't B Don't C Shan't D Won't
E You cannot tell

H56 Lisa Lucky spun a normal 2p coin four times and got TTTT. H means heads and T means tails. If she spins the same coin twice again what will she get?

A HH B HT C TH D TT
E we cannot tell

Puzzling Problems

P1   Ruksana correctly worked out that $3 \times 31 \times 73 = 6789$.
What is the value of $6789 \div 31$?

A 3   B 73   C 93   D 219   E 2263

P2   Each of the calculations below has an answer between 315 and 324
inclusive. Which of the calculations gives an answer closest to 321?

A 11×29 B 12×27 C 14×23 D 15×21 E 17×19

P3   How many factors does 2008 have (including 1 and itself)?

A 2   B 4   C 6   D 7   E 8

P4   If you multiply 123×123, the answer is 15129.
What is the answer to 246×246?

A 246   B 492   C 15 129   D 30 258   E 60 156

P5   I choose a prime number less than 20. I reverse its digits and get
another prime number. I add both prime numbers together and get 88.
What prime number did I first think of?

A 11   B 13   C 15   D 17   E there is no such number

P6   We can write $2009 = 7^2 \times N$. What is the value of N ?

A 7   B 41   C 49   D 287   E 2009

P7   On April Fool's Day our headteacher writes a 6 each
time instead of a 9, and a 9 instead of a 6. Which
number that he writes will be furthest from what it
ought to have been?

A 3096   B 3960   C 6903   D 9063   E 9036

P8   Daisy loves numbers and makes a chain starting with two numbers 2
and 5. She continues the chain, each time adding 1 to the last
number and dividing the result by the one before last. What is the
fourth number in the chain?

A $\dfrac{4}{5}$ B 1   C 3   D 4   E 5

Puzzling Problems

P9 One of these statements is correct. Which one?

    A $266556 \times 655662 = 374664 \times 466473$

    B $366557 \times 755663 = 574664 \times 466475$

    C $166558 \times 855661 = 474668 \times 866474$

    D $566554 \times 455665 = 374666 \times 666473$

    E $966552 \times 255669 = 374665 \times 566473$

P10 What is the value of $(18 \times 4879354) - (17 \times 4879354)$?

    A 0   B 1   C 17   D 18   E 4879354

P11 This magic square is part of a painting by Albrecht Dürer. The missing squares hide two 2-digit numbers which reveal the date the painting was completed. When was the picture painted?

16	3	2	13
5	10	11	8
9	6	7	12
4			1

    A 1316   B 1415   C 1514   D 1613   E 1712

P12 Which of these always describes the answer when you add three consecutive numbers (such as 34, 35, 36) ?

    A even   B odd   C not a multiple of 3

    D multiple of 3   E cannot tell

P13 Moira is 3 years older than her sister Morag and 5 years younger than her sister Muriel. The sum of their three ages is 41. How old is Moira?

    A 10   B 11   C 13   D 18   E 33

P14 Mr Washalot has a café and hangs 15 tea towels on his long washing line as shown.
He could have used two pegs for each tea towel.
How many pegs has he saved by using his method?

    A 14   B 15   C 17   D 20   E 30

P15 If you wrote all the possible three-digit numbers made by using each of the digits 1, 2, and 3 once, what would they add up to?

    A 677   B 738   C 1323   D 1332   E 1350

Puzzling Problems

P16 The value of 99% of 1 000 000 is:

A 99   B 199   C 99 000   D 990 000   E 999 999

P17 Teachers like 'stretching' pupils by giving them hard maths problems. Mona Lotte is stretched from 160cm to 176cm. What percentage stretching is this?

A 6%   B 10%   C 16%   D 60%   E 76%

P18 There is a pole in the lake. One-half of the pole is in the ground under water, another one-third of it is covered by the water, and 2m is out of the water. What is the total length of the pole in metres?

A 4   B 5   C 6   D 8   E 12

P19 My recipe for one serving of fruit smoothie includes $1\frac{1}{2}$ apples, $\frac{1}{3}$ of a banana, $\frac{1}{5}$ of a mango and 5 raspberries. I want to make the smallest possible number of servings without having part of any fruit left over. How many raspberries do I need?

A 10   B 15   C 30   D 150   E 300

P20 If three cats and two kittens weigh the same as two cats and six kittens, how many kittens weigh the same as one cat?

A 2   B 3   C 4   D 6   E 8

P21 Bit + Bot = Bit   Bit + Bit = But   Bit × Bot = Bot

What is But − Bot?

A Bit   B Bot   C But   D Bat   E you cannot tell

P22 Worms have no legs, beetles have 6 legs and spiders have 8 legs. Doug collected worms, spiders and beetles in his garden. Altogether he counted 14 of these creatures with a total of 34 legs. How many of his creatures were worms?

A 2   B 3   C 9   D 14   E 34

Puzzling Problems

P23 This diagram can be completed so that the number in each square is the sum of the numbers in the adjoining circles.

What would the sum of the three numbers in the circles be?

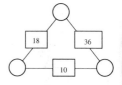

A 22   B 32   C 42   D 52   E There is not enough information.

P24 Dan says, "Half my seven cats are fat". Den says, "A third of my eight dogs are barking". Din says, "A quarter of my nine mice are old". Don says, "A sixth of my 11 tadpoles are wriggling". Dun says, "A fifth of my 10 goldfish are hiding". One is telling the truth. Who is it?

A Dan   B Den   C Din   D Don   E Dun

P25 If $a + b = 6$, $b + c = 8$ and $c + a = 10$, what is the value of a?

A 2   B 4   C 6   D 8   E 10

P26 This mobile has two rods which are both carefully balanced. What value for y will balance the mobile?

A 1   B 2   C 3   D 6   E 12

P27 U, V, W, X, Y and Z are sitting around a round table. U is sitting as shown. Z is sitting next to U and V. X is sitting next to V and Y. Who is sitting opposite U?

A V   B W   C X   D Y   E Z

P28 Which of these shapes cannot be made using six similar matchsticks without breaking them into pieces?

A triangle   B square   C rectangle
D tetrahedron   E hexagon

P29 How many of these shapes will tessellate?

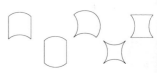

A 1   B 2   C 3   D 4   E 5

Puzzling Problems

P30 Four pieces of curved model railway track will make a full circle. How many of these pieces will be needed for this layout?

A 4   B 6   C 8   D 12   E 16

P31 The sides of this equilateral triangle are divided into thirds. What fraction of the triangle is taken up by the regular hexagon?

A $\dfrac{1}{2}$ B $\dfrac{2}{3}$ C $\dfrac{3}{4}$ D $\dfrac{4}{5}$ E $\dfrac{5}{6}$

P32 How many reflex interior angles are there altogether?

A 6   B 12   C 16   D 18   E 24

P33 Walter Wall is buying carpet at £10 a square metre. How much will carpet for this room cost if there is no carpet left over?

A £140   B £150   C £190   D £200   E £210

P34 How many right angles are there in this diagram?

A 12   B 18   C 24   D 35   E 36

P35 The diagram shows a 'Scoffit' sandwich pack (fraction flavour with added decimals). How many of these packs will fit into a 30cm × 15cm × 12cm box?

A 2   B 4   C 6   D 8   E 12

P36 A solid hexagonal prism is to be painted so that no two faces of the same colour share a common edge. What is the minimum number of different colours required to paint the prism?

A 2   B 3   C 4   D 5   E 6

Puzzling Problems

P37 I make three different straight cuts straight down across the top of my birthday cake. Which of these numbers of pieces is it impossible to get?

A 4   B 5   C 6   D 7   E 8

P38 A robot is moving a boiled egg in three dimensions. For example, [**2, 5, 4**] moves the egg 2 East, 5 North and 4 up.

The egg starts at position (0, 0, 0) and moves [**2, 5, 4**] then [**4, 7, 1**] then [**3, 5, 5**]. What is the position of the egg now?

A (0, 0, 0)   B (2, 5, 4)   C (3, 5, 5)   D (4, 7, 1)   E (9, 17, 10)

P39 My friend Raisa Rouf loves electric socket extensions. The diagram shows one extension plugged into a wall socket. Raisa had seven extensions all plugged in with only one wall socket used. How many sockets were available for use? (**Don't try this at home!!**)

A 7   B 21   C 22   D 23   E 48

P40 Delly, Kelly, Melly, Nelly and Welly have made jellies. They have been tested for wobble. Which jelly wobbles the fastest?

A 4 times in 3 seconds   B 3 times in 4 seconds
C 5 times in 6 seconds   D 6 times in 5 seconds
E 7 times in 7 seconds

P41 A seal called Fara flaps her flippers once every two minutes. Fern flaps her flippers once every three minutes and Fiona flaps her flippers once every four minutes. If they all flap together at 12 noon, when do they next all flap together?

A 12.02 pm   B 12.04 pm   C 12.06 pm   D 12.12 pm   E 12.24 pm

Puzzling Problems

P42 In my room there was one 100 watt light bulb which was on for 5 hours a day. I changed it for a 20 watt low-energy bulb and use it for only 4 hours a day. What percentage of watts is saved each day?

   A 20   B 75   C 80   D 84   E 86

P43 Addum has a digital clock that shows the times from 00:00 to 23:59. From time to time, to help practise his mental arithmetic, he adds the four digits up. What is the greatest total Addum can get?

   A 19   B 24   C 25   D 27   E 36

P44 Five friends wanted to buy the latest Nontindo Wëë Game which normally costs £45.

   Jenny uses a voucher worth 25% off and also a £12 off voucher.
   George uses a voucher worth 20% off.   Harry uses a voucher worth £20 off.
   India uses a voucher taking 1/3 off.   Felix got his for half price.

   Which of the friends paid the least amount of money?

   A Jenny   B George   C Harry   D India   E Felix

P45 A train leaves a station and stops at the next station. Which graph best describes the speed of its journey?

   A   B   C   D   E

P46 Teachers need chocolate. My maths teacher's rule is: 'I eat one then save two for my children, then eat one and save two for my children. This continues until I eat the last one'. If she ate 9, how many chocolates were originally in the box?

   A 9   B 11   C 16   D 25   E 27

P47 Lucky Robbie finds a roll of Scottish bank notes on the floor. Scottish notes are available for £5, £10, £20, £50 and £100. He sees that there are nine notes and that the outside note is worth £100. What is the difference between the largest and smallest amounts he could have found?

   A £140   B £185   C £585   D £760   E £900

Puzzling Problems

P48   This 5 × 5 pattern contains alternating Xs and Os, with an X at each corner.

      How many Xs would a similar 7 × 7 pattern have?

```
X O X O X
O X O X O
X O X O X
O X O X O
X O X O X
```

      A 12   B 13   C 23   D 25   E 50

P49   A café claimed to offer 60 different combinations of children's meals. These children have to eat a main course with vegetables, and a pudding. There were 5 choices of main course and 3 choices of vegetable. How many choices of pudding must there have been for the claim to be true?

      A 3   B 4   C 12   D 45   E 52

P50   Cruella has two pairs of black gloves and three pairs of white gloves mixed together in a drawer. (Left-hand gloves are different to right-hand gloves.) She takes out one glove at a time without looking at it. How many gloves must she take out to be sure of getting a matching pair?

      A 2   B 3   C 4   D 5   E 6

P51   If these numbers are put in order, which one is in the middle?

      A your age in days   B your teacher's height in cm

      C your weight in grams   D your shoe size

      E the height of your classroom in metres

P52   Which of these is most likely to happen to you?

      A There is a spider in your bathroom tonight

      B You win a big lottery prize

      C A friend of yours can eat 30 mince pies in a minute

      D You see a very green sun rise tomorrow

      E Your dog can stand on one leg and say, 'I'm a clever Corgi'.

P53   I have 6 coins in my pocket totalling 99p. I am going to pick a coin at random. Assuming that each coin is equally likely to be chosen, what is the probability that I pick a 20p coin?

      A $\frac{1}{2}$ B $\frac{1}{3}$ C $\frac{1}{4}$ D $\frac{1}{6}$ E impossible to say

Puzzling Problems

P54 Nadia, Natasha, Neeraja, Niku and Noor run a race. Nadia beats Natasha, who is slower than Niku. Noor and Neeraja finish together but not in last place. Who comes last?

A Nadia   B Natasha   C Neeraja   D Niku   E Noor

P55 Last weekend I went to play in a nearby park. It was great fun! I rode my new bicycle that Mum had given me for my birthday. At the park, I saw that there were a total of 17 bicycles and tricycles. If the total number of wheels was 44, how many tricycles were there?

A 3   B 7   C 10   D 11   E 17

P56 A 'down' escalator has 30 steps from bottom to top. It runs at 1 step a second. I am running up it at 4 steps per second. How many seconds will I take to get to the top?

A $8\frac{1}{2}$ B 10 C 12 D 15 E never

P57 Freddie is arranging three identical teddy bears and two identical pandas on a settee to watch TV. The pandas are not allowed to sit next to each other. How many different arrangements are possible?

A 3   B 5   C 6   D 12   E 32

P58 Ronnie Muddle (6 years old) is getting dressed for school. S represents putting on his shirt, T means putting on his trousers, C means putting on his cap, V means putting on his vest and P means putting on his pants. Which of these orders should Ronnie choose for getting dressed?

A CTVPS B STCVP C PSTVC D SPVTC E VPCST

P59 Some children from Stonehenge Primary School are standing in a circle. They are evenly spaced and the fourth child is standing directly opposite the seventeenth child. How many children are there altogether?

A 17   B 19   C 21   D 23   E 26

Puzzling Problems

P60   Five girls think the river looks too cold for a swim. Tammy says she will swim if Debbie does. Holly says she will swim if Sammy does. Sammy says she will swim if Debbie does. Betty says she will swim if Tammy does. Who has to start swimming for them all to swim?

A Betty   B Debbie   C Holly   D Sammy   E Tammy

P61   The monkey chases the weasel up the stairs five steps at a time and has one step left at the top. The weasel chases the monkey down seven steps at a time, and has one step left at the bottom. The number of steps is odd and less than one hundred, so how many steps are there?

A 34   B 35   C 69   D 71   E 101

P62   On average a person visits the toilet 2500 times a year. Older toilets use 9 litres of water per flush but more modern ones use only 6 litres per flush. How many litres of water would a family of four save in a year by using a new toilet instead of an old one?

A 3   B 3 000   C 7 500   D 30 000   E 3 million

P63   Blue balloons need 20 puffs to fill up, yellow balloons need 24 puffs, green balloons need 25 puffs and red balloons need 30 puffs. Puffing Billy puffs all day and uses 990 puffs altogether. If the same number of each colour balloon gets puffed up, how many yellow balloons does Billy puff?

A 10   B 20   C 24   D 25   E 30

Very Puzzling Problems

V1 What is the value of $1 + \dfrac{1}{2} + \dfrac{1}{4} + \ldots + \dfrac{1}{16} + \ldots$?

A $1\frac{7}{8}$ B $1\frac{15}{16}$ C $1\frac{31}{32}$ D 2   E infinity

V2 While eating crisps, Chris Packet reads that the makers claimed to have reduced the amount of saturated fat by 50% from 2006 to 2007 and then to have reduced it by 50% again from 2007 to 2008. There were 0.6g of saturated fat per pack in 2008. How much saturated fat would there have been in 2006 if the claims are true?

A 1.2g   B 1.35g   C 1.8g   D 2.4g   E it is not possible

V3 Tyler Parth, a rich Roman, orders a large mosaic of red strawberries on a black and white patterned background with a total of 24 000 separate pieces. If the number of mosaic tiles needed to make the strawberries is 35% of the total, about how many red mosaic tiles will be needed?

A 4 000   B 8 000   C 10 000   D 12 000   E 16 000

V4 Moths have six legs and spiders have eight legs. How many legs are there in a room with one million moths and seventy spiders?

A 1 000 070   B 6 000 070   C 6 000 008
D 6 000 560   E 60 000 560

V5 In a maths competition (not this one) each correct answer gets three marks, but one mark is deducted for each incorrect answer. Grace answers all 30 questions and scores 30 marks. How many questions did she get wrong?

A 5   B 10   C 15   D 20   E 25

V6 A rumour is spreading through the school. The table shows how many people have heard the rumour after so many minutes.

Time (min)	0	1	2	3
No of people	0	2	8	18

How many people will have heard the rumour after 4 minutes?

A 22   B 26   C 28   D 32   E 40

Very Puzzling Problems

V7 T means a number which is a multiple of 3. S is a number that is one less than a multiple of 3 and U is a number that is one more than a multiple of 3. Which of the following statements is always true?

A U × U = U   B S × U = T   C S × S = T
D S × T = U   E T × T = S

V8 In my street the odd numbered houses are all on one side of the road and the even numbers are on the other side. My house number is a square number. On my left, my neighbour's house is a prime number. On my right, the neighbour's house number is a cubic number (cube). What is my house number?

A 16   B 25   C 36   D 49   E 81

V9 When it was her birthday, my mathematical aunt told me, 'Three years ago my age was a square number. Next year it will be a prime number, and in twelve years it will be a cube number.'
How old is my aunt?

A 28   B 39   C 52   D 84   E impossible to say

V10 The sum of the ages of the five people in the Salter family is 120 years.
The ages of Tom and Sue total 58 years.
The ages of Sue and Dick total 28 years.
The ages of Dick and Jane total 48 years.
The ages of Jane and Harry total 52 years.
Who is the mother and how old is she?

A Sue 35   B Jane 38   Sue 43   D Sue 45   E Jane 52

V11 The large grid of numbers shows part of a 1 - 100 multiplication table. What is the probability of a number chosen at random from this table being an even number?

×	1	2	3	4	5	... 100
1	1	2	3	4		
2	2	4	6	8		
3	3	6	9	12		
4	4	8	12	16		
5						
⋮						
100						

A 0   B $\dfrac{1}{4}$ C $\dfrac{1}{2}$ D $\dfrac{3}{4}$ E 1

26

Very Puzzling Problems

V12 Bob put each of the numbers 1 to 9 into the squares of this diagram. The total in one direction was 15. The total in the other direction was 34. Which number did he put in the centre square?

    A 1   B 2   C 3   D 4   E 5

V13 At full time in a football match, the score was 3 – 2. How many different half-time scores could there have been?

    A 3   B 6   C 9   D 10   E 12

V14 The letters W, X, Y and Z are to be placed in the grid so that each letter appears once in each row, column and the two long diagonals. Which letter will be in the space marked with a *?

    A W   B X   C Y   D Z   E impossible to say

V15 Given that $p = 1$, $p + q = -1$, $p + q + r = 1$, $p + q + r + s = -1$, $p + q + r + s + t = 1$. What is the value of t?

    A –2   B –1   C 0   D 1   E 2

V16 The volcano Sockitome has four vents. Each vent emits coloured smoke and ash regularly but at different intervals: 12min, 16min, 20min and 30min. Once I saw them all blow out lava at the same time. How many minutes did I have to wait to see them blow out lava at the same time again?

    A 60   B 80   C 120   D 160   E 240

V17 Lucy Lycra goes on a long cycle ride. She cycles up a 12 mile hill at 3 mph, then down a 12 mile hill at 12 mph. What percentage of the time does she spend enjoying the downhill part of her ride?

    A 20%   B 25%   C $33\frac{1}{3}$%   D 50%   E 80%

Very Puzzling Problems

V18 If Santa spends one second at each house, approximately how long will it take him to visit 60 million houses?

A 1 min   B 1 hour   C 1 night
D 24 hours   E two years

V19 Lenny and Henry are taking part in a Comic Relief event. They go round a circular path which has a diameter of 7km. At approximately what time would they finish, if they walked at 4km/hr around this path starting at 10am?

A 1.30pm   B 3.30pm   C 5.30pm   D 7.30pm   E 9.30pm

V20 Moira wants to pass a juggling test. She needs to juggle the balls for a mean score of five minutes in five goes. In the first four goes, she juggled for 4min, 5min, 3min and 4min.

How many minutes must she juggle in the fifth go to pass the test?

A 1   B 4   C 5   D 9   E 16

V21 Ickle Pickle goes for a long walk in the Dark Garden. He walks for 15 minutes at 4 km per hour; he steps off the path to talk to the Tumbliboos for $\frac{1}{4}$ hour then goes off along a second path. Poppy Uppy sets off from the same place and along the same path 5 minutes later and walks at 3 km per hour. Where does she find him?

A on the first path   B when he is talking to the Tumbliboos
C on the second path   D in 15 minutes time
E she can't catch him until he stops

V22 The Royal Mint, which makes the UK coins, estimates that there are about £37 million worth of one pence coins lying around in gutters and handbags. If there are 58 million people in the UK, roughly how many pennies each (on average) have we left lying about?

A about 3   B about 64   C about 300   D about 640   E about 3000

Very Puzzling Problems

V23 Erica bought a pencil, a rubber and a ruler for £1. Fritz bought three pens for 75p. Geraldine bought two rubbers and a pen for 45p. Horace bought a pencil, a ruler and a pen. How much did he have to pay?

    A 35p   B 65p   C 85p   D £1.15
    E There is not enough information

V24 What is the angle between the hands of a clock which shows twenty past seven?

    A 70°   B 90°   C 100°   D 110°   E 120°

V25 What is the size of the angle marked × ?

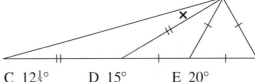

    A 5°   B 10°   C $12\frac{1}{2}°$ D 15°   E 20°

V26 The three lines inside the large triangle are equal in length.
Calculate the size of the angle marked x.

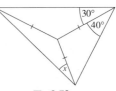

    A 5°   B 10°   C 15°   D 20°   E 25°

V27 A rhombus is divided into two parts S and T as shown in the diagram. Which of the following statements is definitely true?

    A The perimeter of S is equal to the perimeter of T
    B The area of S is smaller than the area of T
    C The perimeter of S is longer than the perimeter of T
    D The area of S is equal to the area of T
    E The perimeter of S is shorter than the perimeter of T

V28 What fraction of the whole tiling is shaded?

    A $\dfrac{1}{2}$ B $\dfrac{2}{3}$ C $\dfrac{3}{4}$ D $\dfrac{5}{6}$ E $\dfrac{7}{8}$

Very Puzzling Problems

V29 The diagram shows a square and a regular pentagon. The area of the square in cm² is the same number as the perimeter of the pentagon in cm. How long is the side *AB* ?

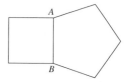

A 4cm   B 5cm   C 7cm   D 16cm   E 25cm

V30 What fraction of the largest circle is shaded?

A $\dfrac{1}{4}$ B $\dfrac{1}{3}$ C $\dfrac{1}{2}$ D $\dfrac{2}{3}$ E $\dfrac{3}{4}$

V31 The diagram shows two oil tanks connected by a pipe. One tank has an 80cm × 80cm cross-section; the other has a 60cm × 60cm cross section.

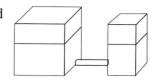

If I pour 100 litres of oil into the larger tank, by how much will the level of oil in the smaller tank rise?

A 1cm   B 10cm   C 20cm   D 25cm   E 100cm

V32 The diagram shows five squares with sides of lengths 5cm, 4cm, 3cm, 2cm and 1cm.
What is the total of the shaded areas in cm² ?

A 3   B 14   C 15   D 55   E none of the other answers

V33 Jemima Puddleduck and Jeremy Fisher swim to and fro across a pool. They start to swim from the middle of adjacent sides at exactly the same time. They swim at the same rate. How far do they swim before they meet?

A They never meet   B 100m   C 105m
D 1050m   E 2100m

V34 In the diagram shown, *PQR* and *PQS* are right-angled triangles. The area of *PQR* is 24cm². What is the area of *QSR*?

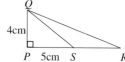

A 10 cm²   B 11 cm²   C 12 cm²
D 13 cm²   E 14 cm²

Very Puzzling Problems

V35 In a quadrilateral, the smallest angle is 28° less than the second smallest, which is 28° less than the third smallest, which is 28° less than the largest.
What is the size of the smallest angle in the quadrilateral?

   A 28°   B 48°   C 90°   D 132°   E 180°

V36 *ABCD* is a rectangle. *E* is half way between *A* and *B*, and *F* is half way between *B* and *C*. What fraction of the whole square is the shaded triangle?

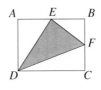

   A $\dfrac{1}{2}$ B $\dfrac{2}{3}$ C $\dfrac{3}{4}$ D $\dfrac{3}{8}$ E $\dfrac{5}{8}$

V37 An equilateral triangle has a perimeter of length 36 cm. Darren makes a straight cut parallel to one of its sides to make a smaller triangle and a trapezium. The two new shapes have the same perimeter.
What is the length of the perimeter of the trapezium?

   A 25   B 26   C 27   D 30   E 33

V38 How many of these cuboids would pass through a 5cm × 6cm hole cut out of a piece of wood?

   2cm × 3cm × 5cm   3cm × 5cm × 6cm
   7cm × 5cm × 4cm   8cm × 7cm × 4cm

   A 0   B 1   C 2   D 3   E 4

V39 Water is poured steadily into this urn which started empty. Which graph best describes how the height of water changes?

Very Puzzling Problems

V40 Dean left his home and cycled on this route: East for three miles, then North for two miles, West for five miles. After a little rest he went North for two miles, East for three miles then South for six miles.
After a drink he went West for three miles and North for two miles. How far and in what direction must Dean travel to get back home?

    A 2 miles East   B 1 mile West   C 3 miles North
    D 5 miles South   E 2 miles West

V41 The numbers on opposite faces on normal dice add up to seven. A die is positioned on a square board as shown. The numbers 1, 2 and 3 are visible. The die is rolled twice, one square south and then one square to the east. Which numbers will you **not** be able to see after the two moves?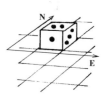

    A 2, 4, 6   B 1, 4, 5   C 1, 3, 5   D 1, 3, 4   E 1, 5, 6

V42 Sean the shepherd has eighteen animal pens. There are sheep in seven of them and goats in nine of them. Four of the pens contain sheep and goats. How many of Sean's pens contain neither sheep nor goats?

    A 4   B 5   C 6   D 7   E 8

V43 William S wrote out the numbers from one to a hundred in English. If he spelt them all correctly how many times did he write the letter V?

    A 20   B 22   C 29   D 31   E 32

V44 Rita Writer's pens can write 24 000 alphabetic letters (a, b, c etc.) before the ink runs out. If she writes eight words to a line, and each word has on average four letters, and there are thirty lines to each page, how many pages will she write?

    A 5   B 10   C 15   D 20   E 25

Very Puzzling Problems

V45 A red squirrel weighs about 300g, which is around 600 times heavier than a Red Admiral butterfly. A red deer weighs 150kg. How many times heavier is the deer than the butterfly?

A 900   B 1100   C 150 000   D 300 000   E 3 000 000

V46 A family of three people each wears a pair of clean socks every day. The washing for several days is put on the washing line. No socks are missing. Which of these numbers could be the number of socks on the line?

A 3   B 15   C 30   D 40   E 45

V47 You have a 350g pack of dried fruit snack. The guideline daily amount (GDA) of fat is 70g. The fruit snack contains 2g fat in 100g. What percentage of the GDA does the pack contain?

A 2%   B 7%   C 10%   D 20%   E 70%

V48 In the grid alongside, you are only allowed to move over the letters right or down (and not diagonally). How many routes through the grid are there which spell the word RHOMBUS?

R H O M
H O M B
O M B U
M B U S

A 1   B 7   C 14   D 16   E 20

Easy Problems – Answers and Notes

E1   **A**   **7 + 3 = 10**

7 + 3 = 10 whilst the others give 73.

Pupils could write more questions like this, showing that there can be many different calculations leading to a single answer.

E2   **D**   **15 + 16**

The other answers are less than 31.

E3   **B**   **12**

It is easiest just to add up in a row, but you could say 2×3s, 2×2s and 2×1s.

E4   **B**   **10**

10 + 2 = 12.

E5   **E**   **48**

48 ÷ 4 = 12.

E6   **D**   **3**

This can be seen without doing the division.

There is a feeling of 'power' when you can calculate something seemingly difficult without actually doing the calculation! Pupils can find remainders of division by 2, 3, 4, 5, 6, 9 and 10 easily. There are lots of easy examples such as: What is the remainder when 43677 is divided by 5? (2)

Here is a harder problem: When I divide 1212121 by 9, what remainder do I get? (1)

E7   **A**   **0**

Any number multiplied by zero equals zero. So don't bother doing any other multiplication here!

Pupils can enjoy making up other complicated calculations which come to zero.

E8   **E** $2 \times 3 + 1$

A is 6, B is 5, C is 0, D is 1.5 but E is 7.

E9   **B**   **hairs**

In any class there are more hairs than other things.

Easy Problems – Answers and Notes

E10 D 14

$12 \rightarrow 24 \rightarrow 28 \rightarrow 14$.

Pupils can make up different sets of rules which give an answer of (say) ten But can they make up a set of rules which always gives ten, whatever the starting number?

E11 A 3

2007 is not even and does not end in 5. It is not divisible by 7. The sum of the digits is a multiple of 3. 3 divides into 2007 exactly.

E12 A 0

The other starting numbers give 3, 9, 18 and 30, not 0.

Pupils could write other problems similar to this, which also end with zero.

E13 C 13

$4 \text{ CLICK } 5 = 4 \times 2 + 5 = 13$.

Pupils could make up other ways of 'CLICKING'.

E14 C 3

Pupils could work through the five responses given or use inverses: + 4 then ÷3. A 'reverse' flowchart can be used.

Pupils can practice and design problems which use inverses. How about these six problems?

		answers
1	+ 3 then – 3 then + 3 then – 3 and my answer is 3.	(3)
2	× 3 then – 3 then × 3 then – 3 and my answer is 0.	(0 or 1)
3	× 3 then ÷ 3 then × 3 then ÷3 and my answer is 3.	(3)
4	× 4 then ÷ 3 then + 2 then – 1 and my answer is 3.	(1½)
5	square the number then square root and my answer is 3.	(3 or –3)
6	subtract from 10 then subtract from ten and my answer is 3.	(3)

E15 B ¼ of 12

The five answers are 4, 3, 4, 4 and 4.

35

Easy Problems – Answers and Notes

E16 C £6.93

Many pupils will calculate 7 × £1 and then take away 7p.
Pupils could try harder prices (e.g. £7.99 each). What about 9 at
£99.99? This idea can be extended to calculations such as 9 × 99,
9 × 999 and so on.

E17 B £6

The difference in the prices is 10p. So the increase is 60 × 10p = £6.
Saving energy and costs are important to us all now. One
example: a bag provided by Severn Trent Water, when placed in
a toilet cistern, will reduce the water used for each flush by 1
litre. They claim that, for a family, the reduction is equivalent to
35 000 cups of tea! Check it out!

E18 E tins per week

The answer for a demonic cat could be 'razor blades per year!'.
Other silly units could be invented for mathematical stories.

E19 E 10

£20 ÷ £2 is 10. Interestingly, in this calculation the pound units
cancel out leaving a 'raw' number as the answer!

E20 B 16

Surjeet must now be 4 and is therefore four years younger than
Gurtek. When Gurtek is 20, Surjeet will be 16.

E21 C 6.45

To see the times, pupils will turn the paper upside down.
Have any pupils seen a clock that goes anti-clockwise, with the
hour symbols arranged accordingly?
Looking at a clock in a mirror makes telling the time difficult.

E22 B 5 h 30 min

6 × 55 minutes is 5 h 30 min. Perhaps your pupils calculated
6 × 1 hr and then took away 6 × 5 min = 30 min to give 5 h 30 min.

Easy Problems – Answers and Notes

E23 D 45

$10 + 9 + 8 + 7 + 6 + 5 = 45$.

Expert players who always knock down all the skittles will calculate their points for different numbers of skittles. Can your pupils work out the number of points with 20 skittles? Can they get a general rule for n skittles? $\left[n \times (n + 1) \div 2 \right]$

E24 D 105

$15 \times 7 = 105$ hours. Playing on a computer for fifteen hours a day is a little excessive. How long do your pupils spend on their computers at weekends?

E25 A 5 miles in 3 hours

The speeds are not all the same. C and D are both 1 mph; B is slower; A is more than 1 mph.

E26 B Thursday

If the day before yesterday was Sunday, today must be Tuesday. So the day after tomorrow will be Thursday.

E27 C 4.9cm

$7\text{mm} \times 7 = 49\text{mm} = 4.9\text{cm}$. (See Guinness Book of Records for the fastest snails!)

E28 A 1.70m

The other heights are much too big!

E29 C 147cm

His height is approximately $7 \times 21 = 147$cm.

E30 D 15cm

There are four gaps between the roses so each gap is $60 \div 4 = 15$cm.

There are many problems related to this. Here is one: there are six fence posts with three lengths of wood between each post. How many lengths of wood are there altogether? A general formula for problems such as this is $N = n(P - 1)$.

E31 A 1mm

Other answers are much too large!

Easy Problems – Answers and Notes

E32 D 36

Elephants have four legs and four feet. $4 \times 9 = 36$.

E33 D 4

There have to be at least 2 teams to have a race. This means that, in a three-legged race, there must be at least 4 people. Some PMC teachers thought this was a 'trick' question and a little unfair.

E34 B 22

These stacks of tins give the triangular numbers: 1, 3, 6, 10, 15, 21, 28, 36, 45 and so on. So 22 could not be one of his stacks of tins.
Pupils could work out how many cans would be in the tenth stack. They might be able to find a general rule for the number of cans in the n th stack: $N = n \times (n + 1) \div 2$.

E35 B very unlikely

It is not impossible that a £1 coin will land on its edge, but it is very unlikely. Feedback told us that some pupils thought the answer should be 'impossible'. But it is possible for a coin to stay upright on its side.
Can pupils think of other events which are extremely unlikely but which could just happen?
Or other events which are almost certain to happen but might not?

E36 C pentagon

The other piece is a five-sided polygon, a pentagon.
If the rule for cutting from one vertex to another is removed, many other remaining shapes can be found.

E37 C nonagon

Pupils could draw other pictures using particular shapes, even create a 3d person using 3d objects.

E38 E pentagon

All the other shapes can be seen in the drawing.

E39 E

From A to E the perimeters are 18, 18, 16, 14 and 12.
Pupils could investigate the perimeter lengths for strips of other lengths, e.g. five units.

Harder Problems – Answers and Notes

H7 C 12

It does not take long to find that $2010 = 2 \times 3 \times 5 \times 67$.

So 6, 10, 15 and 67 are factors but 12 is not.

Are there any other factors of 2010? How about 2011?

PMC papers often have a problem based on the year of the paper. Pupils could work on future years in the hope that there will be a problem in the PMC paper.

H8 A 8

$8 = 2 \times 4$, $14 = 2 \times 7$, $15 = 3 \times 5$, $21 = 3 \times 7$ and $22 = 2 \times 11$. It is not possible to multiply two prime numbers and get 8 as the answer.

H9 E 4

They all equal 1!

What happens if the same pattern continues? What do we get if we remove the last fraction from each block of fractions?

H10 E 99/100

Shading fractions in circles will give 99/100 as the fraction nearest to one. Alternatively, pupils can see how far each fraction is from one: 1/100 is smaller than 1/6, 1/7, 1/8 and 1/24.

H11 A 2

Multiplying the top and the bottom of the whole fraction by 5 gives $(3 + 1)/2$ which is 2. Or divide the top (4/5) by 2/5 to get 2.

H12 C 9

This is $54 \div 6$.

H13 C 1/3

Possibly by saying it (half of two-thirds is one-third!) or by doing a drawing or by using fraction rules!

H14 B 444 444

A, C and E are not divisible by 2, 4 or 6 as they would have to at least be even numbers.

D doesn't end in 0 or 5 so it can't be a multiple of 5. That leaves B. No working needed!

Harder Problems – Answers and Notes

H15 B 3

The two numbers must be 3 and 6 which have a difference of 3.
Pupils could work out other similar problems (unaware that they
are finding roots for quadratic expressions such as $x^2 + 9x + 18$!).
They can find the difference for these problems: sum = 10,
product = 25; sum = 0, product = -16; sum = -10, product = 25;
sum = 6, product = 0.

H16 B 3

5×4 gives 20, with the 2 carried forward. The 5×3 gives 15, so
1 must be carried forward from the middle multiplication. So $5 \times$
* must be 15, with the * = 3.
Of course, $1670 \div 5 = 334$, giving the answer 3 immediately!

H17 C 6

$a = 6$ and $b = 4$. Pupils will probably use trial and error to
work this out.
They could try many others problems like this, with the 10 and
the 2 varying. They could start with these:

$a + b = 10, a - b = 10.$ $a + b = 0, a + b = 10.$
$a + b = 0, a - b = 10.$ $a + b = 10, a - b = 20.$
$a + b = 5, a - b = 0.$ $a + b = 20, a - b = -20.$

Can you always find a and b in any sum like this?
(How about $a + b = 3$ and $a + b = 3$, or $2a + 2b = 6$?)

H18 E 4

Bing $\times$ Bing = Bing, so Bing = 0 or 1. Bing + Bing = Bang,
so Bang = 0 or 2. But Bing and Bang are different numbers – not
both equal to 0. So Bing = 1, Bang = 2 and Bang $\times$ Bang = 4.

H19 C 12

The figures in the problem are all in the 4 times table.

Harder Problems – Answers and Notes

H20 D 51

15 + 17 + 19 = 51.

Pupils may be able to find a quick way to calculate (say) the 20th odd number using the rule $2n - 1$. Of course, to add three consecutive odd numbers, one can just multiply the middle one by 3. Understanding this, pupils could calculate the sum of the five consecutive odd numbers starting with the twenty-eighth odd number! (295)

H21 E all of these

Every year has a New Year's Day and Christmas Day.

H22 C 15

The crate is rectangular so the best number is 15. All the others, being prime numbers, would give long thin crates. What numbers of bottles could be used to make square crates? Or crates that are rectangular and nearly square? Or crates which are nearly square but have a number of bottles next to a prime number?

H23 C 1, 2, 3

$1 + 2 + 3 = 1 \times 2 \times 3$.

H24 C 25

The largest total is 30; the smallest is 5. So the difference is 25.

H25 C 22

Don't forget to add Bill's legs too!

H26 C 22

In 12 days, Ginger lays 12 eggs, Rocky lays 6 eggs and Bunty lays 4 eggs, totalling 22 eggs.

H27 D 20

Five people each give out four cards each, making $5 \times 4 = 20$ in total.

Pupils could move from listing what cards are needed, to creating a formula for calculating how many are needed. How many if, one year, everyone in their class gave each other birthday cards? How many in their school?! How much would that cost at 50p per card?

Harder Problems – Answers and Notes

H28 D £4.50

Each letter of the necklace costs 50p. So Mackenzie's necklace costs 9 × 50p = £4.50.

H29 D 5

Miss Fivefroots needs 56 cherries, which requires 5 packets of 12 (with 4 cherries left over).

H30 C 3

There are 3 such numbers (20, 40 and 80). Numbers that are multiples of four and five must be multiples of 4 × 5 = 20. But beware of 60!

H31 C 20

Pupils might try to guess how many seeds are needed; the numbers work out quite easily: 60% of 20 is 12. Calculating directly, 12 ÷ 0.6 = 20.

H32 B 2p

Another 2p coin will allow all values up to and including 40p. Pupils could try to find a set of coins such that, with one of each coin, all amounts could be made without any gaps. A set of six of these coins (1p, 2p, 4p, 8p, 16p, 32p) will make all numbers up to 63p with no gaps.

H33 B £2.10

The cheapest way is to buy 24 buns for the price of 16 (160p), then 4 for the price of 3 (30p) and then 2 at 10p each (20p). Total is £2.10.

H34 D 500

Pupils will estimate the thickness of a 2p coin, probably in mm. In fact the thickness of ten 2p coins stacked together is almost exactly 2 cm so each coin is about 2mm thick.

Approximately how many 1p coins make up a one metre tower? Other coins?

H35 D 6.5cm

Between 6.15pm and 9.30pm there are 3 h 15 min. 2cm × 3¼ is 6.5cm.

Harder Problems – Answers and Notes

H36 B   96

Mr Average, aged 80, would have used about 80 × 1200m = 80 × 1.2km = 96km of paper.

H37 B   £4

The monk is buying a fifth of a kilo @ £20 per kilo.

H38 B   29 Feb 1996

Harriet was born on 29 February, ten years ago. Information on leap year people can be found at http://www.leapyearday.com/hr/members.html .

H39 D   450

2107 – 2007 = 100. 2107 – 1907 = 200. 2057 – 1907 = 150. So the number of years travelled in total is 100 + 200 + 150 = 450.

H40 B   ¼

The large square can be divided into eight small triangles. Two are shaded so the required fraction is 2/8 or ¼.

H41 C   cylinder

A cone has one curved face and one flat face. A pyramid has five flat faces. A sphere has one curved face. A cuboid has six flat faces. (There was some discussion by teachers about whether a face can be curved – some thought it was incorrect to call the surface of a cylinder or a sphere a face.)

H42 D   ½

An extra line across the centre of the rectangle will show two more triangles the same as the two green triangles. So the total area of the green triangles is a half the area of the flag.
The Guyanan flag is slightly more complicated than the diagram in the PMC paper. Fraction problems can be made from these other flags: Antigua and Barbuda, Benin, Chile, Columbia, Czech Republic, Madagascar, Nigeria, Peru, Spain, Taiwan, Thailand, Trinidad and Tobago, U.A.E., and Ukraine. Pupils could also design flags with mathematical fractional areas!

Harder Problems – Answers and Notes

H43 A 1

Going into the maze and moving one step at a time gets you to exit 1.

By changing the compass directions inside the maze, is it possible to start by the arrow and go through every small square in the maze before coming out? At which exit would you come out? Pupils could draw similar mazes from which you never come out!

H44 E 16

There are 8 slices on the top layer ($360° ÷ 8 = 45°$) and there are two layers in the container so there are 16 mini-cheeses altogether.

H45 D 25m²

The area of the grass that is left is $8 × 5 – (5 × 3) = 25m^2$.

H46 C 2

The first and the third diagrams have rotational symmetry of order 4. The second and fourth have rotational symmetry of order 2.

Pupils can design different 3 × 3 tiles with different orders of rotational symmetry. Can they fit them together to make a larger pattern with particular symmetrical features?

H47 C 24

One side of each of the equilateral triangles (4cm long) will form part of the perimeter of the hexagon; i.e. $6 × 4 = 24$cm.

H48 A cylinder

Cubes, cuboids and pyramids do not have circular profiles; spheres have circles for both side views and plan.

Pupils could draw the elevations and plans for the other shapes in the question, and for shapes such as cones, Toblerone packets and short hexagonal pencils.

Harder Problems – Answers and Notes

H49 D 60°

The equilateral triangle has angles of 60°. The three angles making the straight line including the required angle add up to 180°. By symmetry the other two angles are equal, so the required angle is 60°.

Pupils could calculate all the other angles in this diagram.

H50 D (10)

The perimeters are 14, 14, 12, 10 and 12 so D has the smallest perimeter.

It is satisfying to check this problem using nine squares. Pupils can see easily the 'clustering' of the squares to get a smaller perimeter for the same area. By imagining a very large number of very small squares, we almost get the shape of a circle which has the shortest perimeter for a particular area.

H51 C 57

Counting from the centre gives $1 + 1 + 2 + 2 + 3 + 3 + \ldots + 7 + 7 + 1 = 57$. Or, an 8×8 grid would be filled with 63 connections. So here we will need $63 - 6 = 57$.

H52 D NW

My head rotates anticlockwise through one complete turn, and then 45° more, so my head is now facing NW.

Skate and snow boarders know all about 180° and 360° as well!

H53 E SW

The butterfly flies south at 5mph but also has wind of 5mph towards the west. The result is that the butterfly will actually be flying towards the south west.

Pupils could try to find out (drawing by trial and improvement) in which direction a swimmer (6mph) would have to aim in order to directly cross a river flowing at 3mph.

Can a swimmer (6mph) directly cross a river flowing at 6mph? (No!)

H54 A ƎƆI⅃OԀ

All the letters of the word POLICE have to be reflected.

Harder Problems – Answers and Notes

H55 B   Don't

Diagrammatically, with the pupil arguing the most on the left, the problem gives: Can't → Shan't → Won't → Don't.

Can these other problems be solved (using > meaning 'argues for longer than')?

a) C > D, S > D and W > D

b) C > W and S > D

c) D > W, C > D and D > S

d) C > D, S > W, D > S and W > C!

H56 E   we cannot tell

Whatever the preceding outcomes, the next result cannot be known.

Pupils can methodically list all possible outcomes and calculate the probability of a particular outcome. For example, what is the chance of getting THTH when a coin is spun five times? (answer 1/16)

Puzzling Problems – Answers and Notes

P1   **D**   **219**
We know that $3 \times 31 \times 73 = 6789$, so $6789 \div 31 = 3 \times 73 = 219$.

P2   **C**   **14 × 23**
Pupils could do all the calculations. But they have been told that all the answers are between 315 and 324.
The last digits of the calculations are 9, 4, 2, 5 and 3 which means that 14×23 will be nearest to 321.
(A: 319, B: 324, C: 322, D: 315, E: 323)

P3   **E**   **8**
$2008 = 2 \times 2 \times 2 \times 251$. The factors are 1, 2, 4, 8, 251, 502, 1004 and 2008.

P4   **E**   **60 516**
We know $123 \times 123 = 15129$. We need
$2 \times 123 \times 2 \times 123 = 4 \times 123 \times 123$; i.e. double 15129 twice.
Of course, $246 \times 246 = 60\,516$ directly as well!

P5   **D**   **17**
Reversing 17 gives 71 (also a prime number). Adding gives 88.

P6   **B**   **41**
$2009 = 7 \times 7 \times 41$. So $N = 41$.
Or, $7 \times 7 = 49$, so N must have a unit digit of 1. The answer must be 41!

P7   **E**   **9036**
The differences are: A: 27 (3096 – 3069) B: 270 (3960 – 3690)
C: 2700 (9603 – 6903) D: 2970 (9063 – 6093) and
E 2997 (9036 – 6039). So 9036 is the answer.
There is a logical way to solve this problem. The 9 goes to 6 and the 6 to 9. So the number which is the furthest from what it ought to have been is the number which has the biggest gap between these 9s and 6s, i.e. 9036. Pupils could try this out using other numbers which the head teacher has manipulated!

Puzzling Problems – Answers and Notes

P8 **A** **4/5**

After 2 and 5, we get $(5 + 1)/2 = 3$. So the chain is now 2, 5 and 3. The next number is $(3 + 1)/5 = 4/5$.

Pupils will find that this number chain loops after the fifth term. They could use two different starting numbers with the same rules and see what happens.

P9 **A** **266556 × 655662**

Multiplying the final two digits of any multiplication will give the final digit of the answer. Statement A is the only one of the five to give the same final digit (2) on both sides of the equation. Can pupils write similar questions?

P10 **E** **4879354**

In the sum there are 18 of a big number take away 17 of the same big number. That gives one of the big number.

There are many other problems which look horrendous but which can be simply calculated. Here are a few.

$5 \times 7654321 - 4 \times 7654321$ $4000 \times (56789 - 56788)$

$4566^7 / 4566^6$ $(1001 + 999) \times (1001 - 999)$

$10 - 9 + 8 - 7 + 6 - 5 + 4 - 3 + 2 - 1$

$1 + 2 + 3 + \ldots + 98 + 99 + 100$

P11 **C** **1514**

In this magic square, all columns and rows add up to 34. So the missing numbers are 15 and 14 making the date 1514. This painting is called Melancholia I and is in the British Museum.

P12 **D** **multiple of 3**

The sum of three consecutive numbers will be even sometimes, odd sometimes but always a multiple of 3.

If three consecutive numbers are $n, n + 1$ and $n + 2$. They add up to $3n + 3 = 3(n + 1)$. This is divisible by 3. So the sum of all groups of three consecutive numbers is divisible by 3.

What happens if there are four consecutive numbers? Are there general rules?

Puzzling Problems – Answers and Notes

P13 C 13

Pupils may try out the five possible answers. Or imagine that three times Moira's age minus 3 plus 5 = 41 giving Moira's age to be 13.

P14 A 14

Using two pegs for each tea towel will need 30 pegs. But hanging the tea towels as in the diagram will use only 16 pegs, saving the use of 14 pegs.

P15 D 1332

The list shows six numbers, each column adding up to 12. The total is 1332.

Another way of looking at this is to recognise that, as each digit occurs twice in each position, the required total is the sum of the digits multiplied by 222.

What would the sum of all possible four-digit numbers add up to? All possible five-digit numbers?

```
123
132
213
231
312
321
```

P16 D 990 000

This is not easy as the numbers are difficult. 1% of 1 000 000 is 10 000 so 99% is 990 000.

P17 B 10%

Mona is stretched 16 cm by her teacher. The percentage stretching is $(16 / 160) \times 100 = 10\%$. Don't forget, boys stretch as well as girls!

P18 E 12

One half is in the ground and one-third in the water, so one-sixth is above water. This is 2m. So the total length of the pole is 12m.

P19 D 150

We need an even number of apples, a multiple of 3 bananas, and a multiple of 5 mangos. 30 is the lowest common multiple of 2, 3 and 5, and 30 servings uses $30 \times 5 = 150$ raspberries.

51

Puzzling Problems – Answers and Notes

P20 C 4

$3c + 2k = 2c + 6k$ gives $c = 4k$. But algebra is not needed. Imagine these cats and kittens in a balance (sitting still!). Take away two cats and two kittens from both sides. You would now be left with one cat on the left side, and four kittens on the right.

Pupils could experiment with similar questions using different numbers. Here are a few similar problems with interesting results! In each case, calculate the number of kittens which weigh the same as one cat.

Three cats and two kittens weigh the same as two cats and six kittens. ($c = 4k$)

Three cats and two kittens weigh the same as two cats and two kittens. ($c = 0$)

Three cats and two kittens weigh the same as three cats and one kitten. ($k = 0$)

Three cats and two kittens weigh the same as two cats and one kitten. ($c = -k$!)

Three cats and two kittens weigh the same as three cats and two kittens. ($0 = 0$!)

Some people might think that all this is very silly. But we can enter the world of virtual cats and kittens which is exciting. How do we know this doesn't exist?

P21 C But

Bit + Bot = Bit so Bot must be 0. So, if Bot is zero then But – Bot = But.

P22 C 9

Pupils will work through different combinations of beetles and spiders to get 34 legs (worms are obviously not involved in this). There is only one possible combination: 2 spiders (2×8) and 3 beetles (3×6) = 34 legs. So there are $14 - (2 + 3) = 9$ worms.

Puzzling Problems – Answers and Notes

P23 B 32

The sum of the numbers in the square boxes equals twice the sum of the numbers in the circles.

So the required sum is ½ (18 + 36 + 10) – 32.

There is a very good resource for Arithmogons by Frank Tapson at www.cleavebooks.co.uk/trol/index.htm then select arithmetic practice from the menu.

P24 E Dun

Only whole numbers of pets are allowed! If one person is telling the truth, it must be Dun.

Pupils can make up other statements which cannot be true!

P25 B 4

Pupils may try the suggested answers and find which one works. A more methodical approach is to add the three equations giving $2a + 2b + 2c = 24$. So $a + b + c = 12$. But $b + c = 8$ so $a = 4$.

Or you can add the 1st and 3rd equations and subtract the 2nd to get $2a = 8$ so again $a = 4$.

The trick of adding all three equations can be extended to four, five etc. These equations look very complicated but are easy to solve! Calculate the value of a.

$a + b + c + d = 12 \quad b + c + d + e = 22 \quad c + d + e + a = 32$

$d + e + a + b = 42 \quad e + a + b + c = 52.$

Adding these five equations gives $4(a + b + c + d + e) = 160$, so $a + b + c + d + e = 40$.

Therefore $a = 18, b = 8, c = -2, d = -12$ and $e = 28$.

P26 C 3

12 is balanced by $6 + 6$, so $2y = 6, y = 3$. This has assumed that the lengths of each side of each balance are equal.

Pupils can design other balances using xs and ys. Using just xs, they can write a balance and then an equation which the balance represents. Getting harder, pupils could design balances with unequal lengths of the horizontal rods in the mobile.

Puzzling Problems – Answers and Notes

P27 C X

Z is sitting next to U (and V) so Z is one side or other of U. X is next to V and Y, so X is next to V; i.e. is sitting opposite U. Z could be sitting either side of U – this complicates the solution but does not prevent us solving the problem!

P28 B square

Squares have four equal sides which cannot be made using six matchsticks.

P29 B 2

Two shapes can tessellate (top left and top middle); the others cannot.

P30 D 12

Two curved pieces of track make a half circle, and three make three quarters of a circle. Adding up around the perimeter we get 12 curved pieces of track. This is not easy, but pupils can try to find single loop layouts which use different numbers of the curved track: 4, 8, 16. Must these numbers be a multiple of four? Can any multiple of four above 4 give a closed layout?

P31 B 2/3

If lines are drawn into the illustration to give nine equal triangles, then we see that 6/9 are shaded; so the required fraction is 2/3.

P32 A 6

There are two interior reflex (> 180°) angles in each shape.

P33 C £190

The 'missing' lengths are 7cm and 1cm. The area of the carpet is 19 m^2 so the cost is 19 × £10 = £190. There are of course several different ways of calculating the area of this floor. Pupils could check that they all give the same answer!

P34 E 36

Each rectangle has four right angles (12). There are six intersections with four right angles each (24). The total is 36.

Puzzling Problems – Answers and Notes

P35 E 12

Taking the dimensions of the bottom of the box as 30cm and 15cm, then four packs will fit into the bottom of three layers, making 12 packs in all.

P36 B 3

Two colours will do for the six edges while a third colour will do for the two ends. So three is the minimum number of colours needed.

Pupils could work out the minimum number of colours for other 3-d objects.

P37 E 8

These diagrams show how to get 4, 5, 6 and 7 pieces of cake. It is evident that 7 is the greatest number of pieces in this way, as it requires the greatest number of intersections.

Pupils could find out the different number of pieces of cake with four cuts.

Different numbers of pieces of cake can be obtained if horizontal cuts are allowed as well as vertical cuts. Try it for three and four cuts.

P38 E (9, 17, 10)

As in 2-dimensions, the first coordinates can be added to give the first coordinate of the answer; i.e. 0 + 2 + 4 + 3 = 9. And so on.

This problem is in three dimensions. But mathematicians can use a similar notation to move the egg in four dimensions. Or more!

Puzzling Problems – Answers and Notes

P39 C 22

If the extension leads are used in a row, then each extension has three vacant sockets except for the last one, which has four. That gives the number of sockets available for use as $6 \times 3 + 4 = 22$. But the plugs could be plugged into the extension leads in many different ways, e.g. all four sockets in the first one used.

However, it is always true that there are 29 sockets (including the one in the wall) and 7 of these have plugs in, leaving 22 unused.

Pupils can develop the formula for this problem, in words and then using algebraic symbols: 3 times (the number of extensions − 1) add 4 or, if e is the number of extensions and N the number of sockets available for use, then $N = 3 \times (e - 1) + 4$.

P40 A 4 times in 3 sec

E gives one wobble per second. B and C have less than one wobble per second. A and D have more than one wobble per second, with A wobbling the faster! (A: 1 1/3 w/sec; D 1 1/5 w/sec)

P41 D 12.12 pm

The L.C.M. of 2, 3 and 4 is 12. So the next time the seals all flap together will be at 2.12 pm.

The numbers 2, 3 and 4 have been used in this problem. Pupils could investigate what the answers would have been if 3, 4 and 5 had been used. Or 4, 5 and 6 etc.

P42 D 84%

I used a 100 watt bulb for 5 hours a day. Now I use a 20 watt bulb for 4 hours a day. I am saving $100 \times 5 - 20 \times 4 = 420$ units of energy (watts). The percentage saving is $420 / 500 \times 100\% = 84\%$.

Pupils could do an approximate estimate on lighting in their own house and see how many watts could be saved each day. Each year? With help, they could estimate how much money might be saved in a year.

P43 B 24

When the clock shows 19:59, the sum of the digits is 24.

Puzzling Problems – Answers and Notes

P44 A Jenny

Jenny pays £21.75, George pays £36, Harry pays £25, India pays £30 and Felix pays £22.50.

P45 A

The speed starts at zero, increases, falls and returns to zero between the stations.

Here are a few more 'story graphs' for pupils to sketch.

a) travelling to two stations rather than one.

b) travelling from one station to another but slowing down during the journey.

c) sketching a distance / time graph for a journey from one station to the next.

d) sketching a distance / time graph for a journey stopping at several stations.

e) (hard) sketching the acceleration of a train as it travels from one station to another.

P46 D 25

The teacher eats one and saves two eight times before she eats the last chocolate. So there were 8 × 3 + 1 = 25 chocolates in the box originally.

P47 D £760

The maximum amount of money would be 9 × £100 = £900. The smallest amount of money is £100 + 8 × £5 = £140. So the difference is £900 – £140 = £760. Incidentally, in England the largest bank note is £50.

Puzzling Problems – Answers and Notes

P48 D 25

Most pupils will probably draw the 7 × 7
square and count the Xs.

$$x\ o\ x$$
$$o\ x\ o$$
$$x\ o\ x$$

The diagram shown here has 5 Xs and 4 0s,
totalling 9 (3 × 3). The pattern in the challenge has 13 Xs and 12
0s, totalling 25. For the 7 × 7 pattern the numbers are 25 and 24.
Can you show that, for these patterns, the number of Xs is
always one greater than the number of 0s? If so, then for the 21
square pattern the total will be 21 × 21 = 441, and then the
number of Xs and 0s will be 221 and 220.

In fact if the pattern is an $n \times n$ square, then the number of Xs is
$\frac{1}{2}(n^2 + 1)$ and the number of 0s is $\frac{1}{2}(n^2 - 1)$.

P49 B 4

There were 5 × 3 = 15 choices for main course and vegetable.
There must be 4 choices for pudding as
$$5 \times 3 \times 4 = 60.$$
This café offers 60 choices. Consider cafés that offer three
choices, What other numbers of combinations are possible (up to
about 100)?

P50 E 6

Cruella might take out all the left-hand gloves (5) first before
choosing a right-hand glove or right-hand gloves first before
choosing a left-hand glove. So she has to choose six gloves to
guarantee a pair.

P51 B teacher's height

These are rough estimates:

> your age is about 365 × 10 or 11 (about 3650);
> your teacher's height in cm is about 170cm;
> your weight is very approximately 35kg = 35 000g;
> your shoe size is approximately 6;
> and the height of your classroom about 3m.

Putting these in order, the middle one is 170 which is your
teacher's height.

Puzzling Problems – Answers and Notes

P52 A spider

The probability of winning the lottery, eating 30 mince pies in a minute, seeing the sun looking green and your dog on one leg are all extremely small. The spider is more likely than any of these. Again, pupils can make up situations which are impossible, very unlikely, most likely and certain.

P53 B 1/3

To make 99p with 6 coins means that the coins must be 50p, 20p, 20p, 5p, 2p and 2p. So the probability of selecting a 20p at random will be 2/6 = 1/3.

Pupils could try 41p with three coins, or 88p with six coins.

If £1.18 were made up of six coins, what is the probability (assuming each coin is equally likely to be picked) of picking a 20p coin? Are there any problems with this problem? (Yes! There is more than one way of getting £1.18 with six coins, and there are no 20p coins anyway!)

P54 B Natasha

Natasha is slower than Nadia and Niku. And the other two come together but not last. So Natasha is last.

P55 C 10

Pupils could draw up a table like this.

No of bikes	1	2	3	4	5	6	7
No of trikes	16	15	14	13	12	11	10
No of wheels	50	49	48	47	46	45	44

Using algebra, $3t + 2(17 - t) = 44$ giving $t = 44 - 34 = 10$.

P56 B 10

I gain $4 - 1 = 3$ steps a second, so it will take $30 \div 3 = 10$ seconds.

Puzzling Problems – Answers and Notes

P57 C 6

Here are the possible arrangements, given in a systematic order:

TTPTP	TPTTP	PTTTP
TPTPT	PTTPT	PTPTT

Pupils could find the number of arrangements if the pandas are allowed to sit together, or could explore the possibilities when there are different numbers of teddies and pandas.

More difficult is a similar problem but with teddies and pandas that are not identical. For example the teddies might be wearing different coloured hats and the pandas different scarves.

P58 E VPCST

Ronnie needs to put his vest on before his shirt and his pants before his trousers. His cap can go on at any time!

Pupils could list the other ways Ronnie could have dressed himself but there are a lot of them ($5 \times 4 \times 3 \times 2 \times 1 = 120$)! How many different results are possible; i.e. how many ways could Ronnie look after dressing in different ways? Pupils could create other situations which provide chaos when operations are done in the wrong order.

P59 E 26

There are 12 between the fourth and seventeenth children, with 12 more the other way round. So in total there are 26 children.

Given different numbers in the question (4th and 17th), pupils could find a rule with which to calculate the number of children in the circle, firstly by writing a sentence describing the rule, and then possibly using algebra and a and b.

Puzzling Problems – Answers and Notes

P60 B Debbie

If Debbie says she will swim then so
will Tammy (and so will Betty), and
Sammy (and so will Holly).

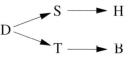

Who has to start swimming in these cases? Draw arrow diagrams
to show what happens.

a) Tammy will if Debbie will. Debbie will if Holly will. Holly
will if Sammy will. Sammy will if Betty will. Betty will if
Tammy will.

b) Tammy will if Debbie will. Holly will if Sammy will. Debbie
will if Tammy will. Sammy will if Holly will. Betty doesn't
want to swim.

P61 D 71

Multiples of both five and seven (< 100) are 35 and 70. Add one
to these (36 and 71) and choose the odd number (71). This is
easy, as five and seven do not share common factors; it would be
harder than this if they did.

P62 D 30 000

Each flush of the newer toilet saves 3 litres of water. The family
will flush the toilet about 2500 × 4 = 10 000 times each year, so
10 000 × 3 = 30 000 litres of water would be saved if a newer
toilet was being used. Of course it would be better to recycle
used bath water instead of using drinking water.

P63 A 10

Blowing up one balloon of each colour takes 99 puffs. So, to use
up 990 puffs altogether, ten of each colour were blown up.

Very Puzzling Problems – Answers and Notes

V1   D   2

The sum gets closer and closer to 2 as the number of terms gets larger. So the total for an infinite number of terms is 2.

There might be a discussion on whether it is possible to continue to infinity. Some will say that it is impossible, and say that the answer must be less than two. But if you could continue to infinity, the answer would then be two. If a mathematician met this series in higher maths, (s)he would have no hesitation in giving the answer two.

Pupils could draw two squares, shading in the fractions as they look along the series. This shows that the sum gets closer and closer to, but not greater than 2.

What happens if they shade in fractions in this sum? $1 + 1/2 + 1/3 + 1/4 + 1/5 + ... $.

V2   D   2.4g

Reducing a figure by 50% one year means halving it. The same again for the second year. So reducing the figure by 50% one year and again the next year will 'quarter' it. Going from 2008 back to 2006 therefore, we multiply by 4. So in 2006 there would have been $0.6 \times 4 = 2.4g$.

V3   B   8 000

The number of red tiles needed is 35% of 24 000. Pupils can do the percentage calculation. Or they might see that 10% is 2 400, so $3½ \times 2 400$ are required. 8 000 is the nearest number suggested.

V4   D   6 000 560

One million moths with six legs each gives 6 000 000 legs. Seventy spiders, each with eight legs gives 560 legs.

Very Puzzling Problems – Answers and Notes

V5 C 15

Pupils might use trial and improvement. The answer is that Grace gets 15 wrong (and 15 correct) giving her 15 × 3 − 15 × 1 − 30 marks.

An equation could be used. If x is the number of *incorrect* answers, than $3(30 − x) − x = 30$. This gives $90 − 3x − x = 30$, so $4x = 60$ and so $x = 15$.

V6 D 32

The differences between the number of people hearing the rumour are 2, 6 and 10. So 4 is being added each time. The next difference will be 14. So after 4 minutes $14 + 18 = 32$ people will have heard the rumour. The formula $n = 2t^2$ gives the relationship.

How long will it take 100 people to hear this rumour, according to this rule?

Is this a realistic rule for rumours? Are there limits to the usefulness of this rule?

V7 A $U \times U = U$

Pupils will probably choose some numbers and see if the formulae work. For example, A works if U is 4 as $4 \times 4 = 16$ (one more than a multiple of 3). B doesn't work if S is 8 and U is 10. C doesn't work if S is 6. D doesn't work if S is 5 and T is 6. And E doesn't work if T is 6.

Algebra can be used to test statement E. If U is a number which is one more than a multiple of 3 then we can write U as $3n + 1$. $U \times U$ is therefore $(3n + 1)(3n + 1) = 9n^2 + 6n + 1$. Both $9n^2$ and $6n$ are multiples of 3 so $9n^2 + 6n + 1$ is one more than a multiple of 3 and therefore a number described by U. This is hard for primary pupils but nice for the teachers!

Very Puzzling Problems – Answers and Notes

V8 B 25

The houses next to my house are two lower and two higher than my house number. So I am looking for a square number with my neighbour's numbers being prime and cubic. The square numbers are 1, 4, 9, 16, 25, 36, 49, 64, 81 and 100. If my house number is 25, I would have a prime number one side (23) and a cubic number (27) the other. So the numbers go 23, 25 and 27.

Pupils could make up other similar problems using house numbers in their street.

V9 C 52

Square numbers are 1, 4, 9, 16, 25, 36, 49, 64, 81 and 100. So she is 4, 7, 12, 19, 28, 39, 52, 67, 84 or 103.

If her age is a prime number next year she must be either 4, 12, 28 or 52. Cube numbers are 1, 8, 27, 64 and 125. She must therefore be 52 years old as 52 + 12 = 64 (cube number).

V10 B Jane 38

The ages of the five people add up to 120. T + S = 58. D + J = 48. So T + S + D + J = 106.

That means that H = 120 – 106 = 14. We can now calculate everyone's age: H = 14, J = 38, D = 10, S = 18 and T = 40. So Jane is the mother and is 38 years old. There will be many different ways to solve this problem.

V11 D ¾

In this large table, half will be even and half odd. When multiplied together, even × even, even × odd and odd × even will give even answers. Only odd × odd gives an odd response. So three-quarters of the answers will be even.

If two random numbers chosen from this table are added together, what is the probability of an even number? If subtracted? What would happen if the table did not stop at 100 across and down, but continued for ever? Would this change the answers?

V12 D 4

The sum of the numbers from 1 to 9 is 45. The sum of the two lines is 49. So the number which is in both lines (i.e. counted twice) must be 4.

Very Puzzling Problems – Answers and Notes

V13 E 12

The list of possible scores is (0, 0), (0,1), (0,2), (1, 0), (1, 1), (1, 2), (2, 0), (2, 1), (2, 2), (3, 0), (3, 1), (3, 2). That is twelve different scores.

Pupils can work out how many different half-time scores there are for other final results. If this is done systematically, they might be able to spot the formula – for final results of a, b there will be $(a + 1)(b + 1)$ half time-scores. Can they 'justify' the formula?

V14 D Z

The table can be completed using the four different letters in every row, column and long diagonal.

W	X	Y	Z
Z	Y	X	W
X	W	Z	Y
Y	Z	W	X

V15 E 2

If $p + q + r + s = -1$ and $p + q + r + s + t = 1$, then $t = 2$.
The first three equations are not needed in this calculation. (In fact $p = 1$, $q = -2$ and $r = 2$.)
If the pattern in this problem continued using the alternating 1 and −1, is there a pattern in the values of u, v, w etc.?

V16 E 240

This problem requires the lowest common multiple (LCM) of 12, 16, 20 and 30. Pupils could guess intelligently or work through prime factors: $12 = 2^2 \times 3$; $16 = 2^4$; $20 = 2^2 \times 5$; $30 = 2 \times 3 \times 5$. The LCM is $2^4 \times 3 \times 5$. So the volcano blows out lava through all vents at the same time after 240 minutes.

V17 A 20%

Going uphill takes Lucy four hours. She cycles downhill in one hour. Total 5 hours. So the proportion of the time spent enjoying the downhill section is 1/5 = 20%.

This problem shows why cyclists often feel that they are cycling uphill most of the time. They are!

Try these. Calculate the percentage of time enjoying the downhill ride:

4 miles uphill at 4 mph then 4 miles downhill at 12 mph (25%)

6 miles uphill at 4 mph then 6 miles downhill at 12 mph (25%)

6 miles uphill at 4 mph then 6 miles downhill at 36 mph (10%)

Very Puzzling Problems – Answers and Notes

V18 E two years

Thinking directly about how many years this will take, we have
60 000 000 ÷ (60 × 60 × 24 × 365).
There follows a difficult cancelling estimation which gives an
answer of approximately 2.
Wittgenstein says that mathematics depends on the form of life.
Maths is like a rhizome, a motley of different cases of rule-
following, invented not discovered. So it might depend on which
universe Santa inhabits and what the local maths rules are!
Pupils can discuss ways of estimating the answer by choosing
different methods of cancellation.

V19 B 3.30pm

The circular path with 7km diameter has a circumference of
approximately 21 or 22km. At a speed of 4km/hr it would take
around 5½ hours. Starting at 10am, the boys would finish at
about 3.30pm.

V20 D 9

For a score of five minutes in five goes, Moira needs 25 minutes
successful juggling. After four throws she has 4 + 5 + 3 + 4 = 16
minutes. So she needs to juggle for nine minutes in her fifth go.

V21 B when he is talking to Tumbliboos

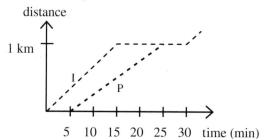

The distance-time graph shows movements for I (Ickle Pickle)
and P (Poppy Uppy). They clearly meet when Ickle Pickle is
talking to Tumbliboos.

V22 B about 64

£37 millions shared between 58 million people is approximately
£40 ÷ 60 which is 4000p ÷ 60 ≈ 67p.

Very Puzzling Problems – Answers and Notes

V23 D £1.15

Fritz bought three pens for 75p so one pen is 25p. Geraldine bought two rubbers and a pen for 45p so a rubber is 10p. Erica bought a pencil, a rubber and a ruler for £1 so a pencil and a ruler (together) cost 90p.

So Horace, buying a pencil, a ruler and a pen, will pay 90 + 25 = £1.15.

Can we ever know how much each pencil and each ruler cost in this problem? No! This has echoes of Q22 (PMC November 2004) in which we never knew how many flies Sylvester caught. Pupils could try to write other problems in which the answer can be found but which leave other questions unanswered.

V24 C 100°

The minute hand is on '4' and the hour hand between '7' and '8'. The angle between '4' and '7' is 90°.

The hour hand is 20/60 = 1/3rd of the way between the '7' and the '8'; i.e. 10° past the '7'. So the total angle is 90 + 10 = 100°.

There are harder problems of this type, but they all use similar techniques to get the solution. Pupils could look for very hard examples of this and see if they can always get the answer!

V25 D 15°

The equilateral triangle on the right has angles of 60°. The middle triangle therefore has angles of 120°, 30° and 30°. So the triangle on the left has angles of 150°, 15° and 15°.

Pupils might like to create geometry problems in which, given only the size of one angle, they can now calculate the sizes of lots of other angles!

Very Puzzling Problems – Answers and Notes

V26 D 20°

Completing the diagram using the
equal base angles of the three
isosceles triangles, we have $x = 20°$.
Here are other diagrams (not to scale)
in which pupils can calculate the sizes
of all the angles.

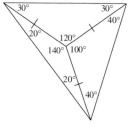

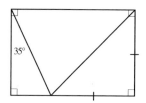
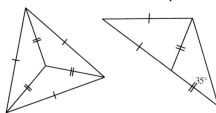

V27 A equal perimeter

Nothing about the areas can be definitely stated. But the
perimeters of the two shapes will be the same however the
rhombus is divided. Each shape has a top or bottom and a side of
the rhombus plus the common zig-zag line.

V28 C ¾

Suppose we take the area of one triangle as one unit of area. The
triangles have an area one-sixth of the hexagons, so each
hexagon has an area of 6 units. Pupils may add up all the
triangles and hexagons to get the fraction shaded as $120 \div 160 =$
¾. Each hexagon has two triangles 'attached' to it so counting
across the whole diagram is not necessary!

V29 B 5cm

If ℓ is the length of side AB, then (numerically) $5\ell = 12$. This
means that $\ell = 0$ or 5. The side AB must be 5cm long.
Pupils could play with the idea of shapes such as squares or
triangles having zero area. A triangle with sides 10cm, 10cm and
0cm has area zero. Is it actually a triangle or a line?

Very Puzzling Problems – Answers and Notes

V30 C ½

The area of each of the two small circles is ¼ of the area of the large circle as the ratio of areas is the square of the lengths. So the fraction of the large circle which is shaded is ½.

The ratios of areas and volumes is a difficult concept. But pupils will gain an understanding by doing the calculations with simple shapes (e.g. squares and rectangles for areas, cubes and cuboids for volume).

V31 B 10cm

The depth in the tanks is equal both before and after the oil is poured in. The cross-sectional areas are $80 \times 80 = 6400$ and $60 \times 60 = 3600$ cm^2. 100litres = 100 000cm^3. If the increase in the depth is $h$cm, then $6400h + 3600h = 100\,000$ so $h = 10$cm.

V32 C 15

Start with the outside square with area 25cm^2. Subtract the area of the next square (16cm^2), add the area of the next (9cm^2), subtract the area of the next (4cm^2) and add the area of the smallest (1cm^2). That gives $25 - 16 + 9 - 4 + 1 = 15$.

Pupils could investigate a rule for calculating the shaded areas for similar designs of different sizes, starting with the simplest (1×1 square in a 2×2 square) and working up. A simple rule can be found (3, 6, 10, 15, 21 …).

V33 C 105m

If the animal swimming lengths swims 105m (a length and a half – ending up in the centre of the pool), the other swimmer will do three and a half widths (105m). They will meet in the middle of the pool.

Can pupils find any dimensions for pools (length and width) such that Jemima and Jeremy would never meet? Perhaps they can find rules which describe dimensions of pools for which Jemima and Jeremy meet and do not meet.

V34 E 14cm^2

The area of $\triangle PQR$ is 24cm^2 and the height is 4cm so the base PR is 12cm. Therefore SR is 7cm; the area of $\triangle QSR$ is $\frac{1}{2} \times 7 \times 4$ which gives 14cm^2.

Very Puzzling Problems – Answers and Notes

V35 B 48°

The four angles of all quadrilaterals add up to 360°. If $s°$ is the smallest angle, we can form the equation

$s × (s + 28) + (s + 56) + (s + 84) = 360$.

So $4s + 168 = 360$; $4s = 192$ giving $s° = 48°$.

V36 D $\frac{3}{8}$

Triangle AED is a quarter of the rectangle. $\triangle DCF$ is also a quarter of the rectangle and $\triangle EBF$ is one eighth of the rectangle. So the shaded area is $1 - \frac{1}{4} - \frac{1}{4} - \frac{1}{8} = \frac{3}{8}$.

V37 C 27

Most pupils will probably use trial and error, and the answer does come easily.

Suppose the new triangle has sides of 6 cm. The perimeters of the triangle and trapezium will be 16 and 30. Not equal! So suppose the lengths of the sides of the new triangle are 9 cm. That gives the perimeters as 27 cm and 27 cm. Equal!

If the two new perimeters were not equal, the problem would have been harder. Suppose the triangle had a perimeter twice that of the trapezium. We could use algebra to form an equation. Suppose the length of the sides of the newly formed equilateral triangle are x cm in length. The total length of the sides of the triangle is then $3x$. The lengths of the sides of the trapezium are x, $12 - x$, 12 and $12 - x$, simplifying to $36 - x$. The equation is therefore $3x = 2(36 - x)$. This gives $x = 14.4$ cm, and the perimeter of the trapezium $36 - 14.4 = 21.6$ cm.

Pupils could try the same problem but with a different initial rule.

V38 D 3

We have to turn around the cuboids to make it as easy as possible to get them through the hole. All can pass through except the 8cm × 7cm × 3cm cuboid. We need at least two of the three dimensions to be smaller than the hole or at least very slippery, if the dimensions are equal.

Pupils can write down a rule for deciding what cuboids will pass through the hole. If the sides of the cuboids are very accurately made, maybe a cuboid with one dimension of (say) 5cm will just be able to pass through a hole with 5cm width.

Very Puzzling Problems – Answers and Notes

V39   A

The urn started empty so the height of the water at the beginning
was zero. So graphs C, D and E are incorrect. The height of the
water will increase faster at the beginning and the end of the
pouring, so the best graph is A.

The vase could be of a different shape, producing a different
graph when filled.

Here are four shapes for pupils to consider.

V40   A   2 miles East

Working out his movements North and South gives a net change
of zero (N for 2, N for 2, S for 6 then N for 2). Movements East
and West give a net movement of 2 miles West (E for 3, W for 5,
E for 3, W for 3). So Dean must travel 2 miles East to get home.

V41   C   1, 3, 5

The die rolls south, covering the 1 and exposing the 6. It then
rolls east, covering the 3 and exposing the 4.

So the 2, 4 and 6 can be seen, and the 1, 3 and 5 hidden.

V42   C   6

A Venn diagram can
help here. Four pens
have both sheep and
goats, so three have

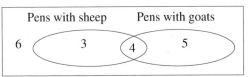

only sheep and five have only goats. That gives 6 with neither
sheep nor goats. Pupils could experiment with different numbers
in their Venn diagrams.

V43   D   31

The letter V occurs in 5, 7, 11, 12, 17, 25, 27, 35, 37, 45, 47, 55,
57, 65, 67, 70, 71, 72, 73, 74, 75 (twice), 76, 77 (twice), 78, 79,
85, 87, 95, 97. Altogether there are 31 Vs.

Very Puzzling Problems – Answers and Notes

V44 E 25

On each page she will write $8 \times 4 \times 30 = 960$ letters. The number of pages will be $24\,000 \div 960 = 25$ (after lots of cancelling!)

V45 D 300 000

The butterfly is ½ gram, so 2 butterflies would be 1g, so 2000 would be 1kg. $150 \times 2000 = 300\,000$.

V46 C 30

Three people will wear six socks each day. So the total number of socks on the line must be a multiple of six.

V47 C 10%

The fruit snack contains $3.5 \times 2 = 7$g of fat. The GDA is 70g of fat so the pack contains $7/70 = 10\%$ of fat.

V48 E 20

Pupils will have to be systematic in working out how many routes there are through the grid.

Pupils could create a rectangle similar to the diagram in this question, but containing numbers rather than letters. The numbers in each position are found by working out the number of ways to get from the top left to the position

1	1	1	1
1	2	3	4
1	3	6	10
1	4	10	20

concerned. This is part of Pascal's Triangle turned through 45° anticlockwise. The rectangle starts as shown. This rectangle can be used for shorter words (e.g. one) and longer words. It can be expanded as far as needed.

The Primary Mathematics Challenge

The problems in this book are taken from the Primary Mathematics Challenge (PMC) papers from November 2006 to February 2010.

The PMC is aimed at school pupils aged 11 or less. In September and October, schools order packs of ten challenge papers (which include Answers and Notes and certificates for everyone). Pupils take the challenge at any time during the month of November. The top scoring pupils are then invited to take the PMC Finals in the following February. Questions from these finals are included in this book. For further information, visit the PMC pages on the MA website (www.m-a.org.uk). The problems set in the PMC Finals are very difficult for primary-aged pupils, and therefore will also challenge younger secondary pupils.

Thanks

This book was compiled by Peter Bailey. Many teachers have worked on PMC problems over the years. Thanks go to Colin Abell, Meryl Hargreaves, Lesley Jones, Rudolf Loewenstein, Robyn Pickles, John Place, Alex Voice and Margaret Williams. Thank you to Robyn Pickles, Colin Abell, Lesley Jones and Pat Bailey for problem selection, lots of ideas and checking the drafts. Thanks also to Bill Richardson for his work on the PMC and in formatting this book.

Challenge your pupils 2
using problem-solving questions from the Primary Mathematics Challenge

This book contains over 200 multiple choice problems which aim to interest and motivate pupils. There cover a full range of mathematics topics and are provided with answers, notes and follow-up ideas. The problems can be used by both primary (and secondary) teachers in class, for homework, and maths clubs.

The problems are taken from the Primary Mathematics Challenge papers from 2006 to 2010. They are presented in four categories - Easy, Harder, Puzzling and Very Challenging. Most pupils between the ages of 9 and 14 should be able to answer the problems in the Easy and Harder sections, but many problems in the Puzzling and Very Challenging sections will challenge the brightest pupils in both primary and secondary schools.

ISBN 978-0-906588-72-7
© 2012 the Mathematical Association

PUBLISHED BY

The Mathematical Association
259 London Road
Leicester
LE2 3BE
Tel: 0116 221 0013
Fax: 0116 212 2835
Email: office@m-a.org.uk

www.m-a.org.uk

MATHEMATICAL ASSOCIATION

supporting mathematics in education

Members of the Mathematical Association are people teaching mathematics to students across the whole age range from nursery school to 'A' level and beyond. We  offer a wide range of professional development opportunities from regional and national one-day events and local branch meetings to annual conferences. Our regular journals include *Mathematics in School*, *Primary Mathematics*, *Equals*, the *Mathematical Gazette*, *SymmetryPlus* and *Mathematical Pie*.

Being an MA member will help you maintain your enthusiasm for teaching mathematics and enable you to keep abreast of developments in mathematics education. Be part of a professional network committed to improving the experience of mathematics for *all* learners.